Based on the best-selling keyboard method *by K*

THE COMPLE
KEYBOARD PLAYER

Great Film Themes

Wise Publications
part of The Music Sales Group
London/New York/Paris/Sydney/Copenhagen/Berlin/Madrid/Tokyo

Master Chord Chart

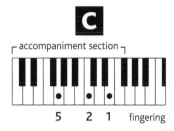

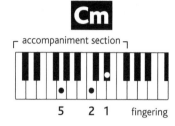

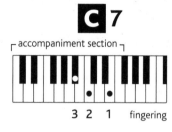

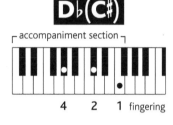

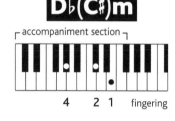

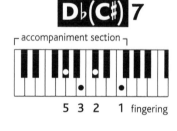

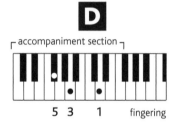

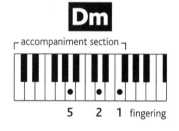

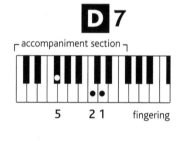

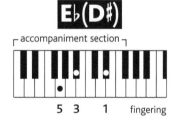

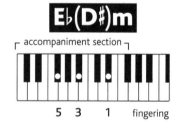

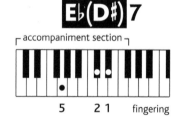

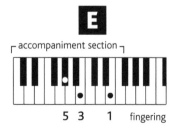

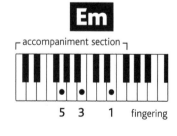

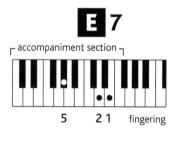

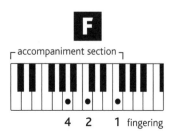

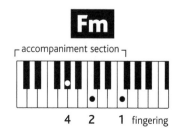

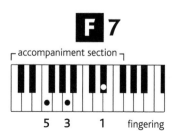

Master Chord Chart

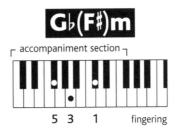

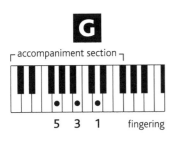

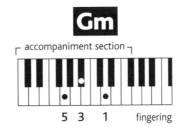

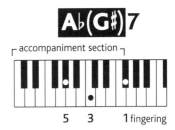

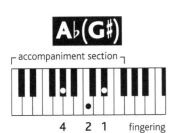

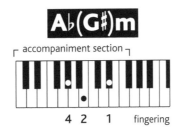

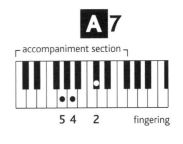

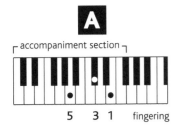

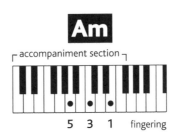

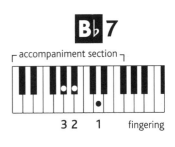

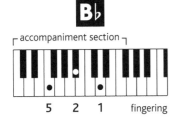

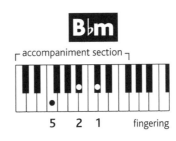

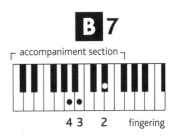

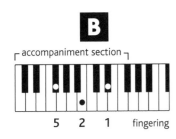

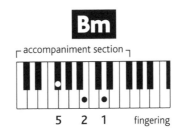

3

Published by
Wise Publications
8/9 Frith Street, London W1D 3JB, UK.

Exclusive Distributors:
Music Sales Limited
8/9 Frith Street, London W1D 3JB, UK.
Music Sales Pty Limited
120 Rothschild Avenue, Rosebery, NSW 2018, Australia.

This book © Copyright 2006 Wise Publications,
a division of Music Sales Limited.
Order No. AM984434
ISBN 1-84609-305-8

Compiled by Nick Crispin.
Music arranged by Paul Honey.
Music processed by Paul Ewers Music Design.
Cover photograph (Shakespeare In Love) courtesy of
Miramax Films/Universal Pictures / The Kobal Collection / Sparham, Laurie.

Printed in the EU.

Your Guarantee of Quality
As publishers, we strive to produce every book
to the highest commercial standards.
This book has been carefully designed to minimise awkward
page turns and to make playing from it a real pleasure.
Particular care has been given to specifying acid-free, neutral-sized paper
made from pulps which have not been elemental chlorine bleached.
This pulp is from farmed sustainable forests and was produced with special
regard for the environment. Throughout, the printing and binding have been
planned to ensure a sturdy, attractive publication which should give years of enjoyment.
If your copy fails to meet our high standards, please inform us and
we will gladly replace it.

www.musicsales.com

Jean de Florette (Theme)

Music by Jean-Claude Petit

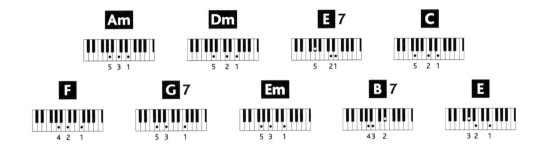

Voice: **Harmonica**
Rhythm: **8th beat**
Tempo: **Rather slow** ♩ = 74

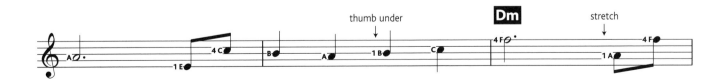

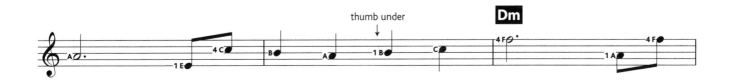

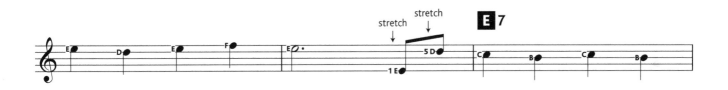

Chinatown (Love Theme)

Music by Jerry Goldsmith

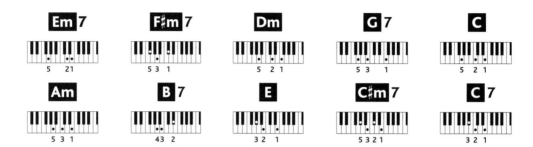

Voice: **Trumbet**
Rhythm: **Ballad**
Tempo: **Moderately** ♩ = 98

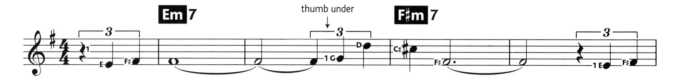

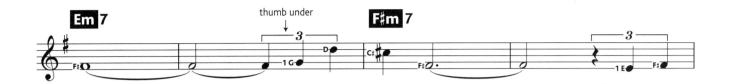

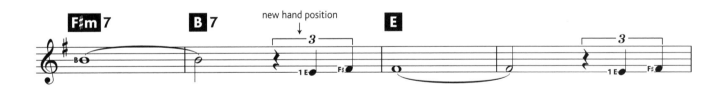

9

The English Patient

Music by Gabriel Yared

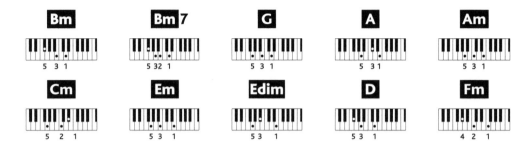

Voice: **Cor anglais**
Rhythm: **Waltz**
Tempo: **Very slow** ♩ = 70
Synchro start: **On**

new hand position
3rd finger over

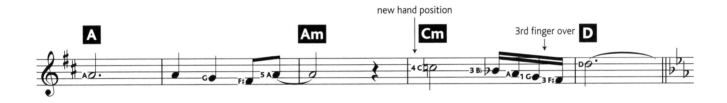

Theme From E.T. (The Extra-Terrestrial)

Music by John Williams

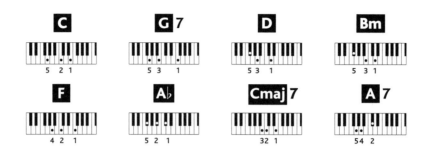

Voice: **Strings**
Rhythm: **Waltz**
Tempo: **Moderately** ♩ = 90

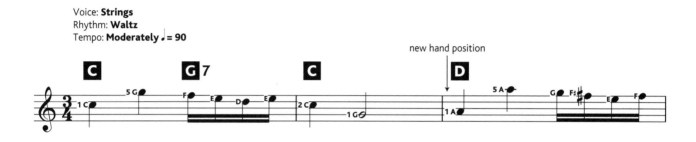

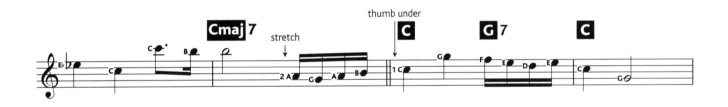

The Godfather (Love Theme)

Music by Nino Rota

Voice: **Mandolin**
Rhythm: **8th beat**
Tempo: **Quite slow** ♩ = 74

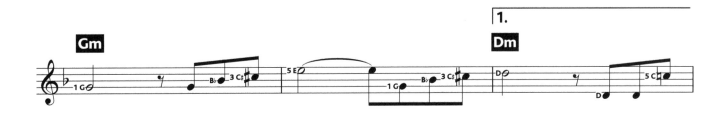

Jurassic Park

Music by John Williams

Voice: **Flute**
Rhythm: **8th beat**
Tempo: **Rather slow** ♩ = 62
Synchro start: **On**

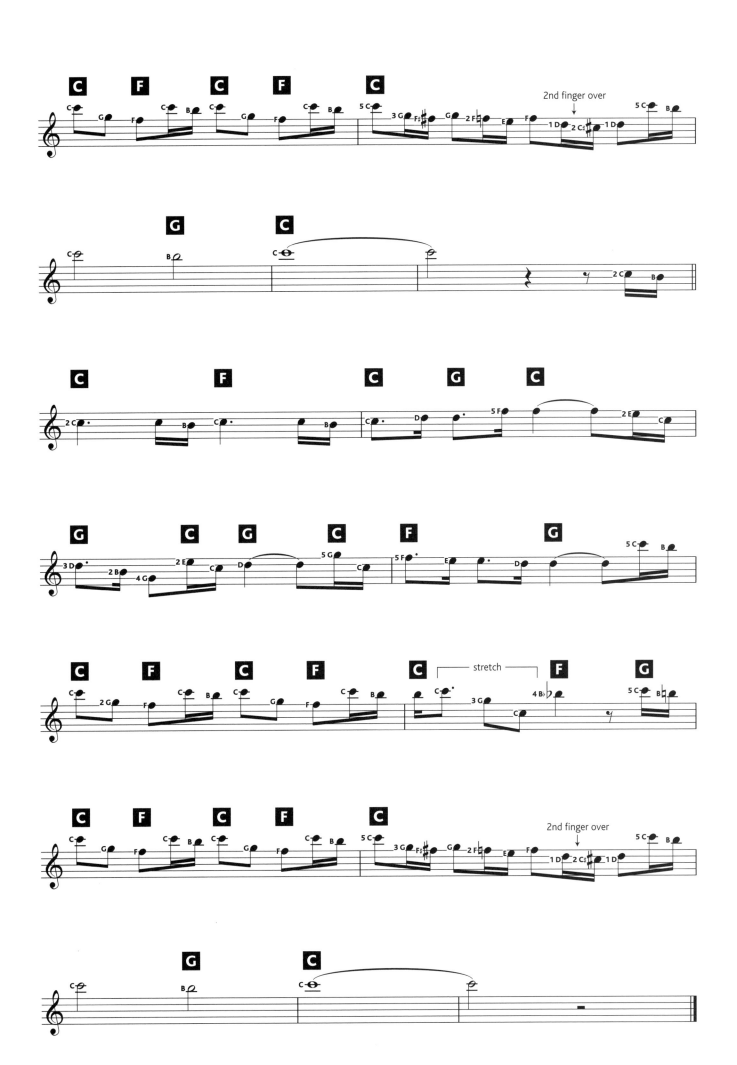

The Last Of The Mohicans

Music by Trevor Jones

Voice: **Strings**
Rhythm: **16th beat**
Tempo: **Not too fast** ♩ = 98
Synchro start: **On**

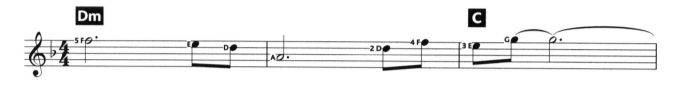

new hand position

new hand position

19

new hand position

new hand position

Love Story (Theme - Where Do I Begin?)

Words by Carl Sigman. Music by Francis Lai

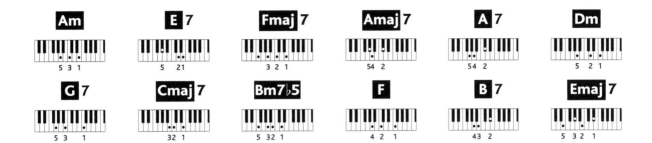

Voice: **Clarinet**
Rhythm: **Soft rock/Bossa nova**
Tempo: **Gently** ♩ = 86
Synchro start: **On**

Where do I be - gin_____ to tell the sto - ry of how

great a love can be._____ The sweet love sto - ry that is

old - er than the sea. _____ the sim - ple truth a - bout the

love she brings to me? She fills my heart. _____ She fills my

heart _____ with ve - ry spe - cial things _____ with an - gel

songs, _____ with wild i - ma - gin - ings. _____ She fills my

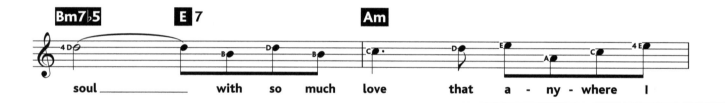

soul _____ with so much love that a - ny - where I

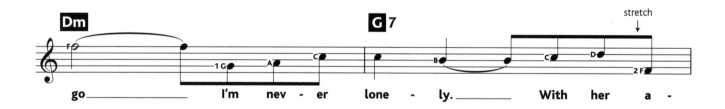

go _____ I'm nev - er lone - ly. _____ With her a -

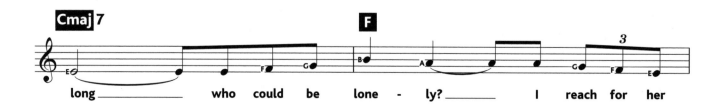

long _____ who could be lone - ly? _____ I reach for her

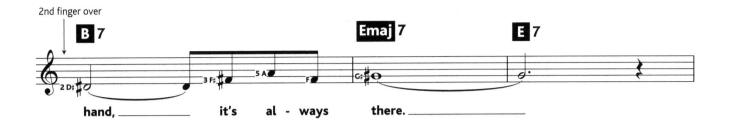

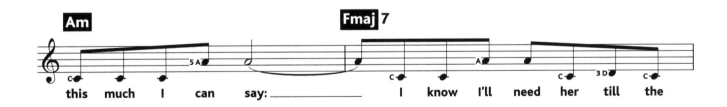

Moulin Rouge! (Closing Credits - Bolero)

Music by Steve Sharples

Voice: **Strings**
Rhythm: **8th/rock beat**
Tempo: **Moderately** ♩ = 108

sempre staccato

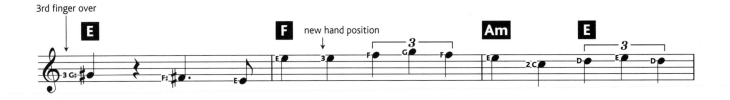

Out Of Africa

Music by John Barry

Voice: **Strings**
Rhythm: **8th beat**
Tempo: **Quite slow** ♩ = 70

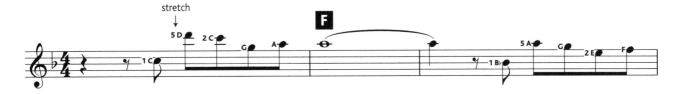

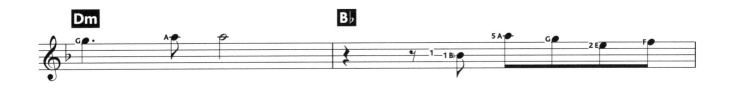

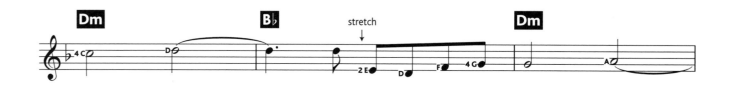

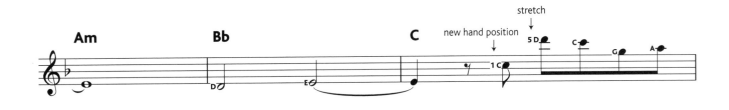

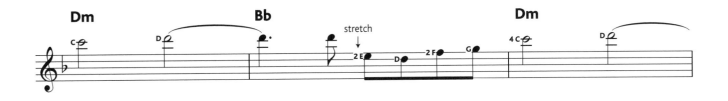

Once Upon A Time In The West

Music by Ennio Morricone

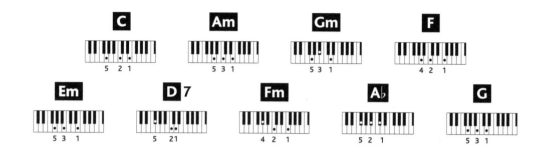

Voice: **Strings**
Rhythm: **?**
Tempo: **Slow** ♩ = 70

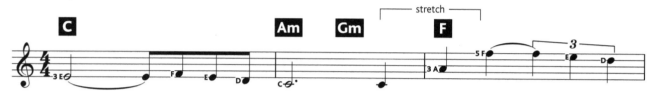

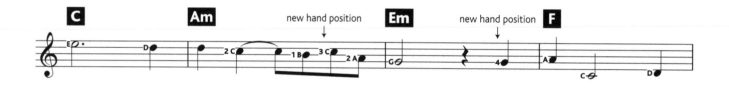

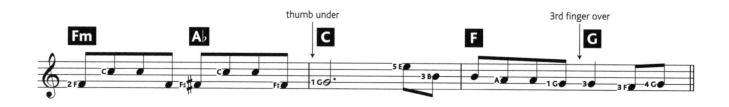

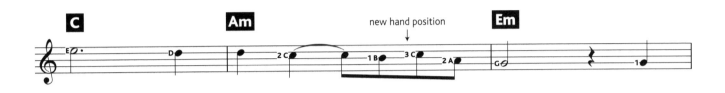

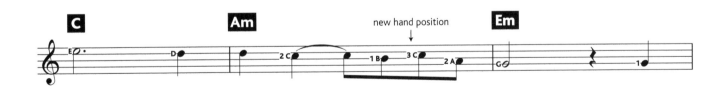

Romeo & Juliet (Love Theme - A Time For Us)

Words by Eddie Snyder & Larry Kusik. Music by Nino Rota

Voice: **Oboe**
Rhythm: **8th beat**
Tempo: **Quite slow** ♩ = 80

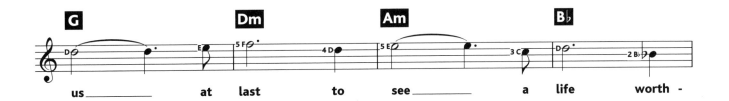

us _____ at last to see _____ a life worth -

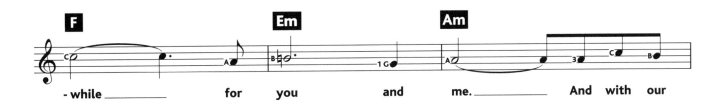

- while _____ for you and me. _____ And with our

love _____ through tears and thorns, _____ we will en - dure _____ as we pass

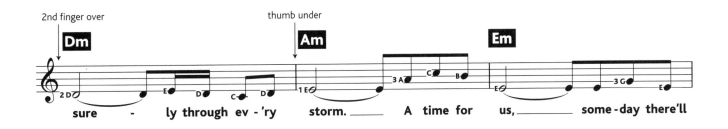

2nd finger over

thumb under

sure - ly through ev - 'ry storm. _____ A time for us, _____ some - day there'll

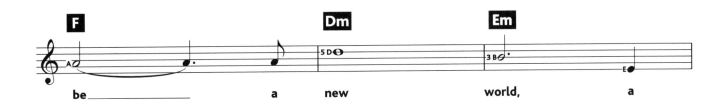

be _____ a new world, a

world _____ of shin - ing hope for you and me.

Schindler's List

Music by John Williams

Voice: **Violin**
Rhythm: **?**
Tempo: **Slowly** ♩ = 62

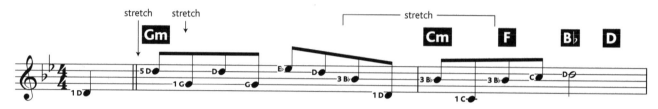

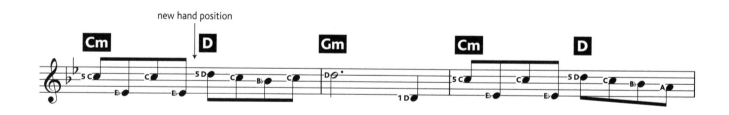

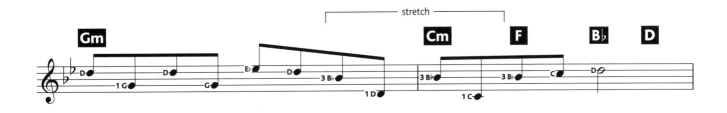

35

The Beginning Of The Partnership (from 'Shakespeare In Love')

Music by Stephen Warbeck

Voice: **Oboe**
Rhythm: **16th beat**
Tempo: **Not too fast** ♩ = 72
Synchro start: **On**

new hand position

Raiders Of The Lost Ark (Raiders March)

Composed by John Williams

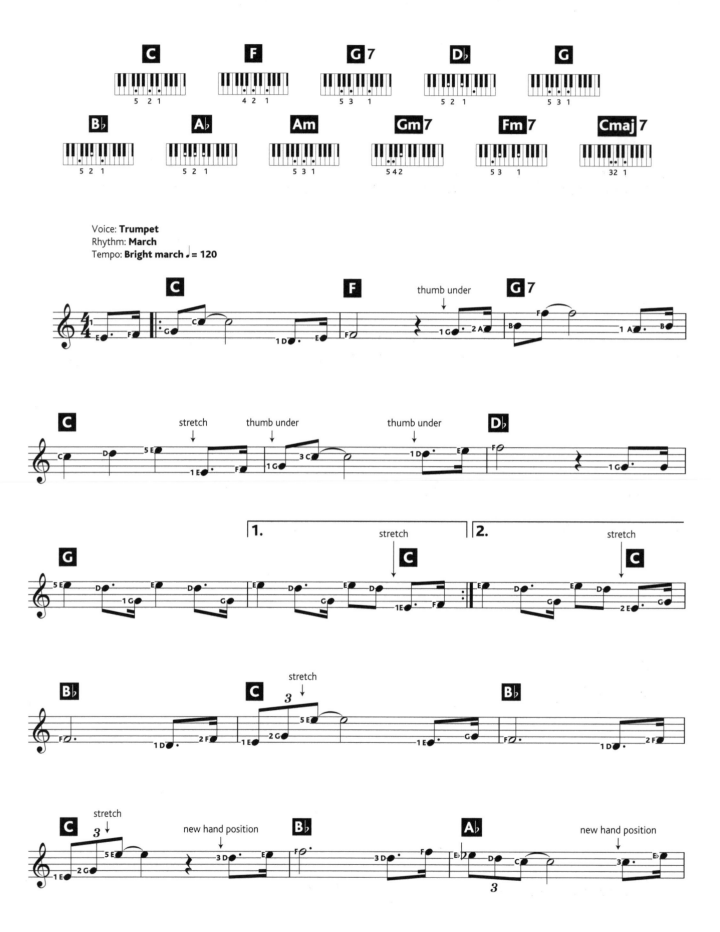

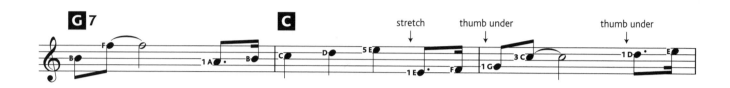

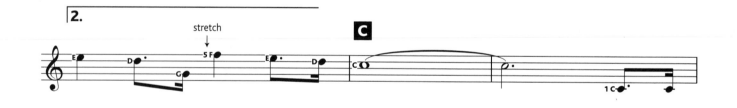

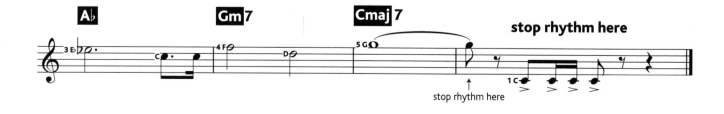

123456789